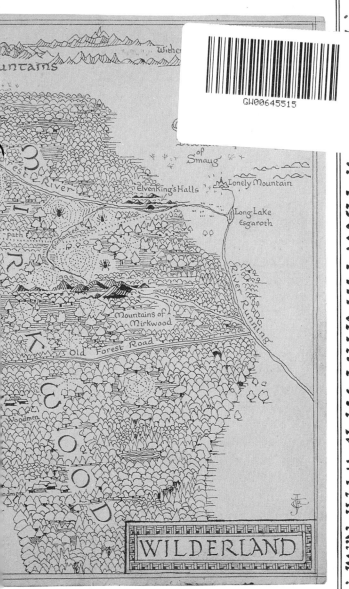

WILDERLAND

THE HOBBIT
Birthday Book

GraftonBooks
A Division of HarperCollins*Publishers*
77–85 Fulham Palace Road,
Hammersmith, London W6 8JB

Pubished by GraftonBooks 1991
The Hobbit Birthday Book
© HarperCollins*Publishers*, 1991

All illustrations are taken from *The Hobbit*
by J. R. R. Tolkien © George Allen & Unwin
(Publishers) Ltd 1937, 1951, 1966, 1978

 © 1990 Frank Richard Williamson
and Christopher Reuel Tolkien,
executors of the estate of the late
John Ronald Reuel Tolkien

A CIP catalogue record for this book
is available from the British Library

ISBN 0-261-10229-X

Printed in Hong Kong

TOLKIEN

THE HOBBIT
Birthday Book

GraftonBooks

A Division of HarperCollins*Publishers*

Bilbo awoke one morning ...

JANUARY

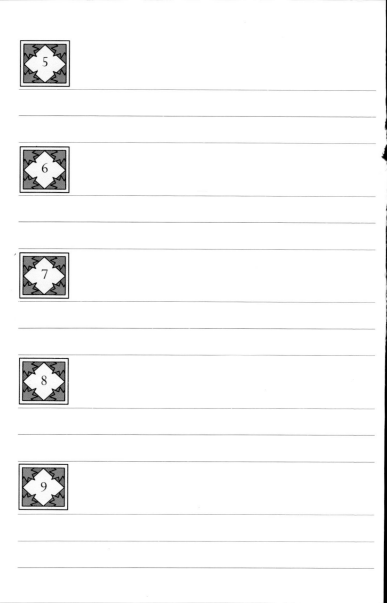

15

16

17

18

19

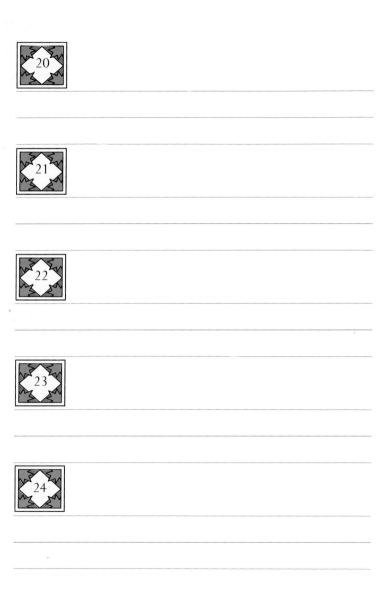

25

26

27

28

29

The Front Gate

FEBRUARY

1

2

3

4

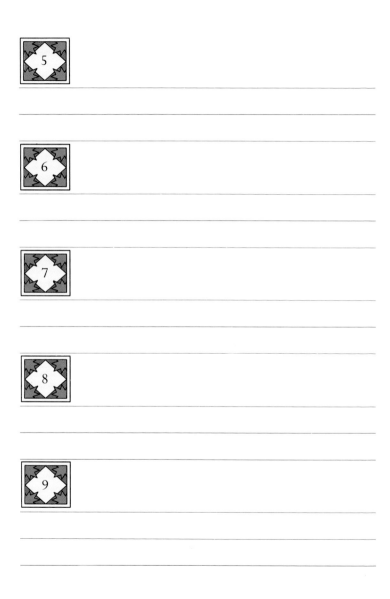

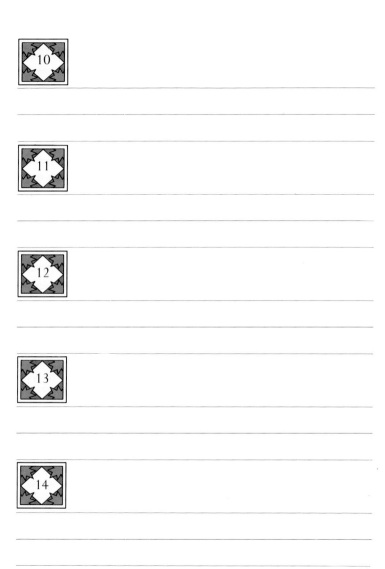

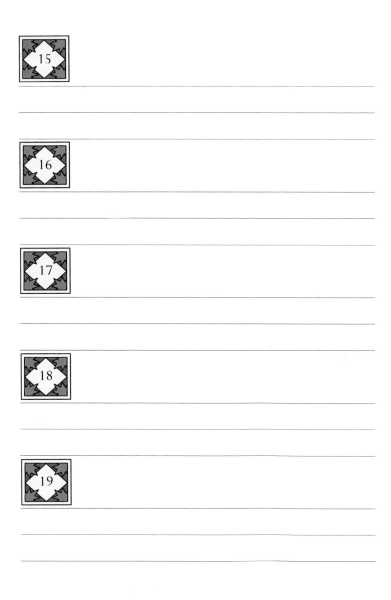

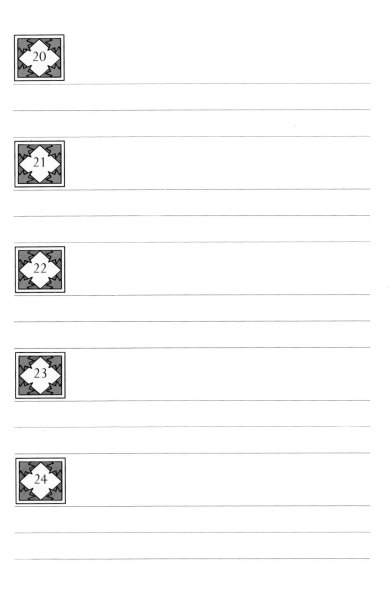

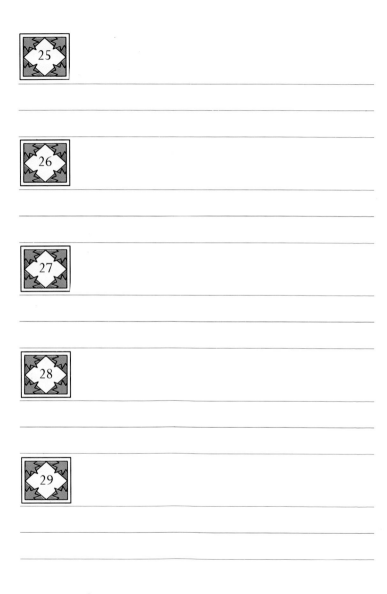

MARCH

1

2

3

4

Bilbo Comes to the Huts of the Raftelves

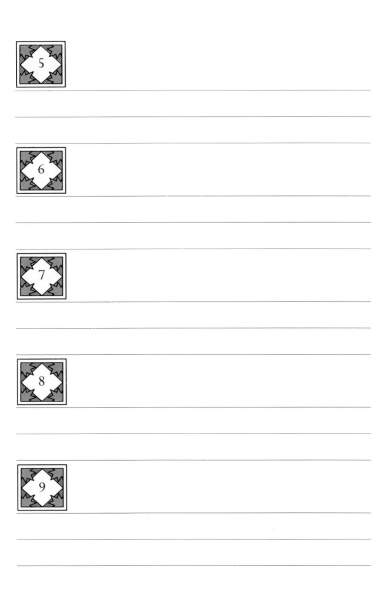

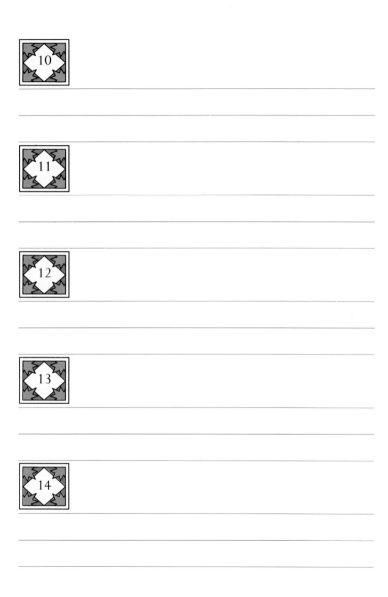

15

16

17

18

19

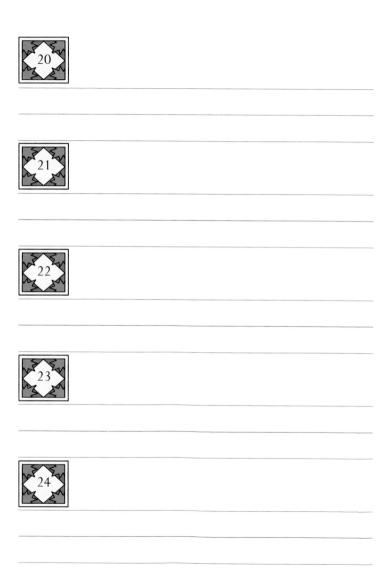

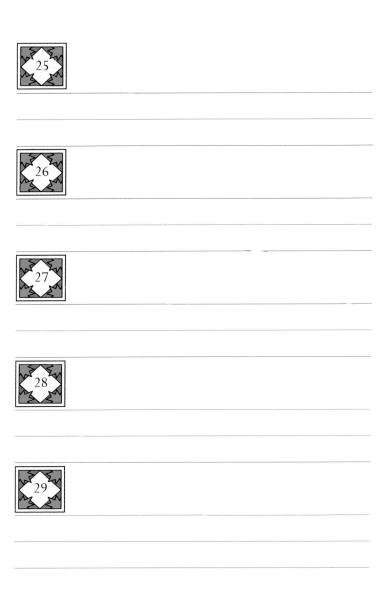

30

31

APRIL

1

2

3

4

Conversation
with
Smaug

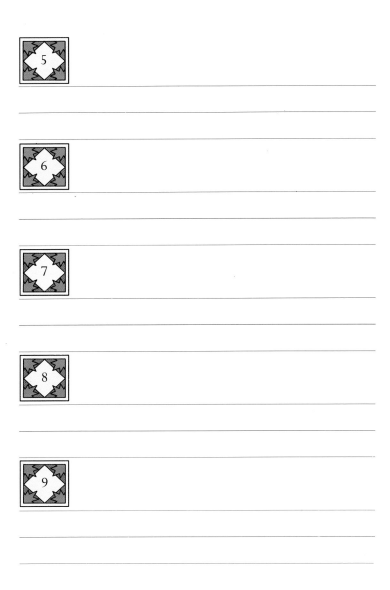

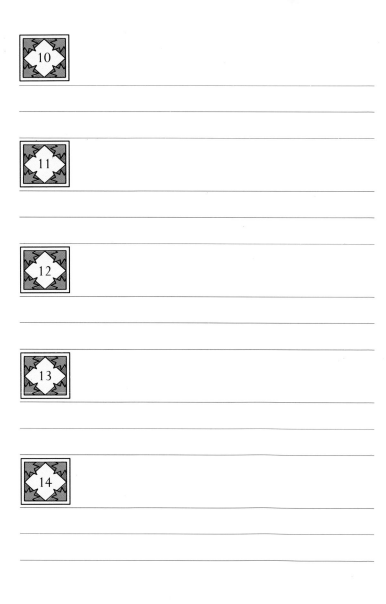

15

16

17

18

19

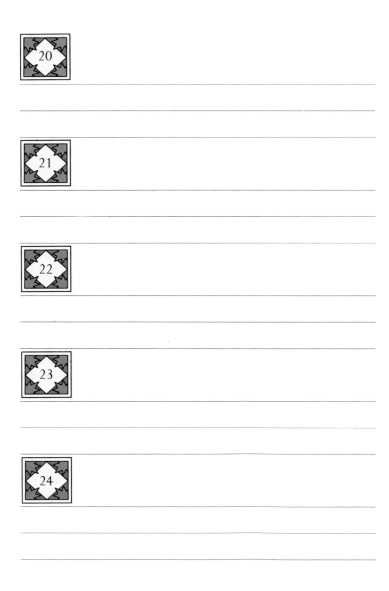

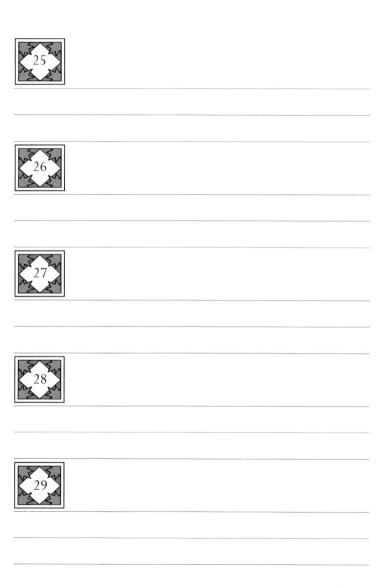

30

MAY

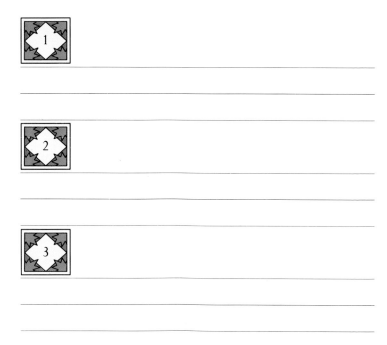

1

2

3

The Hill: Hobbiton-Upon-The-Water

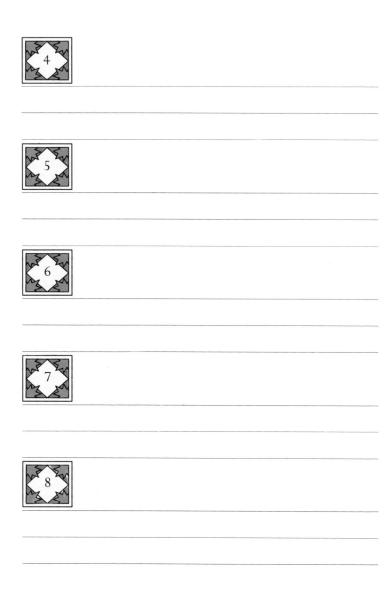

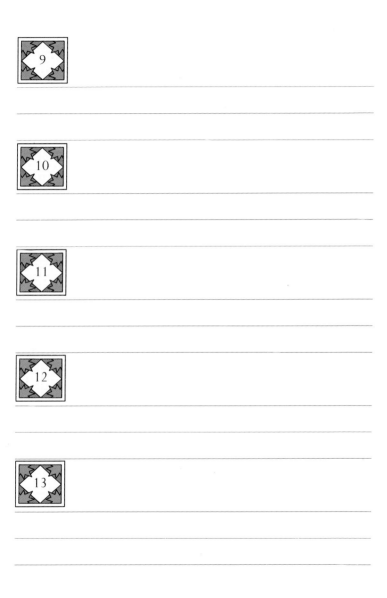

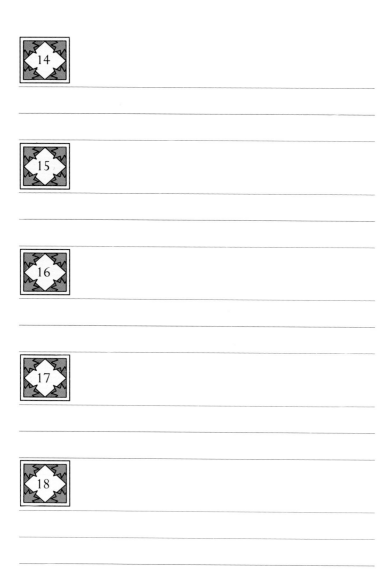

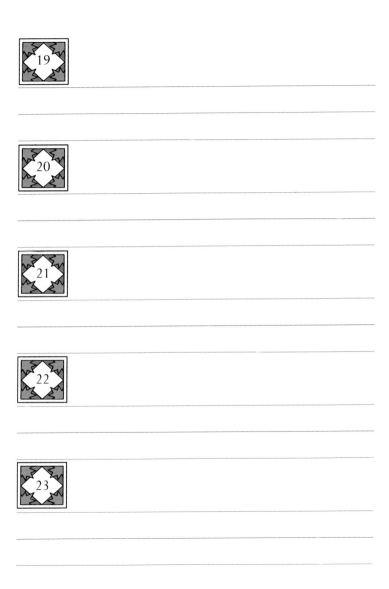

24

25

26

27

28

29

30

31

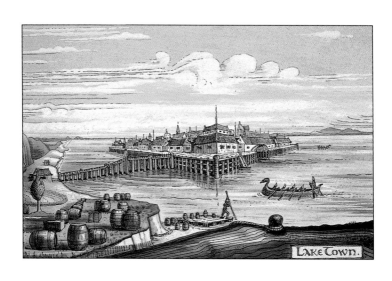

LAKE TOWN.

JUNE

1

2

3

4

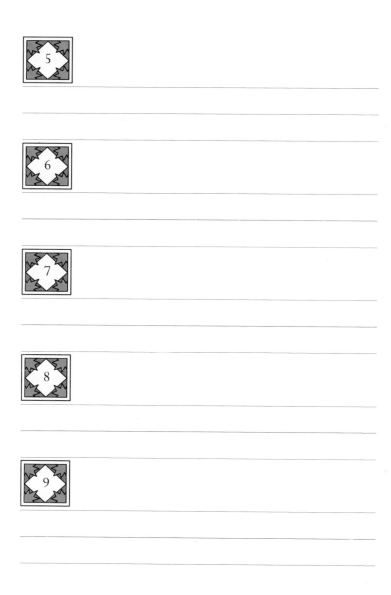

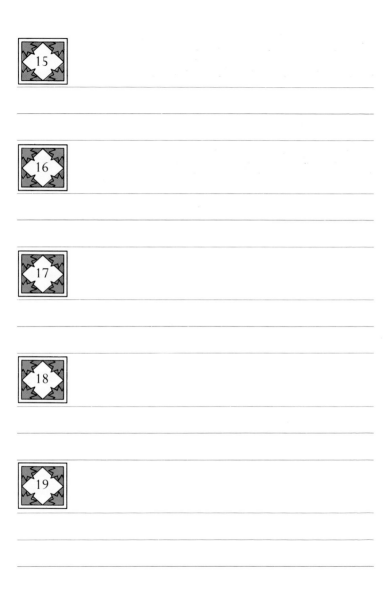

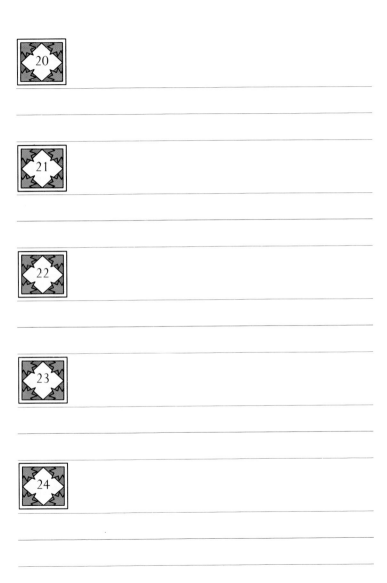

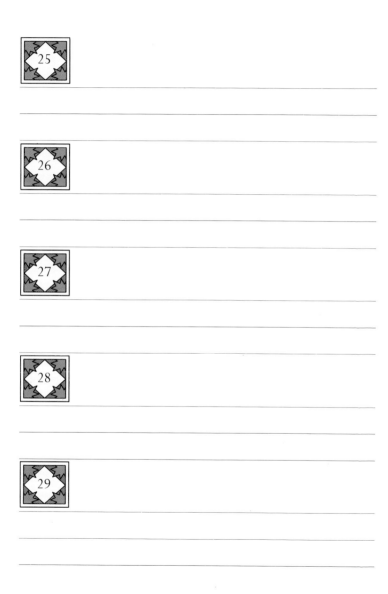

30

JULY

1

2

3

The Elvenking's Gate

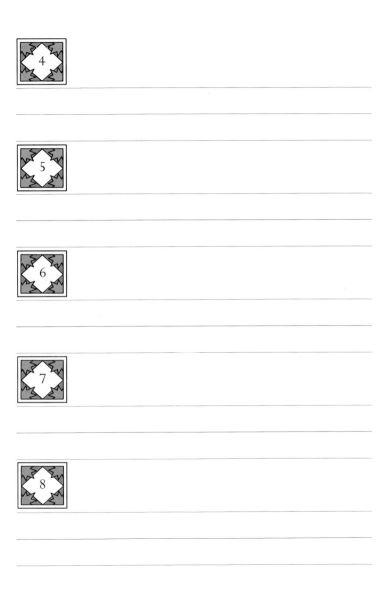

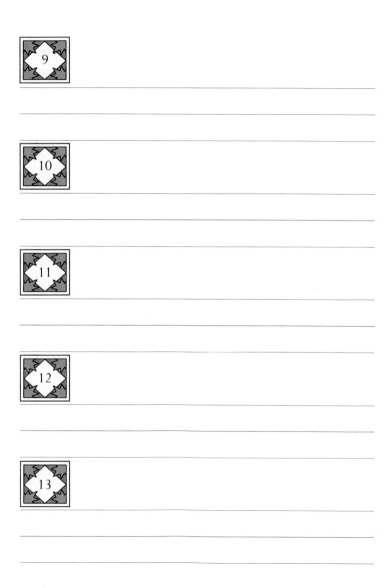

14

15

16

17

18

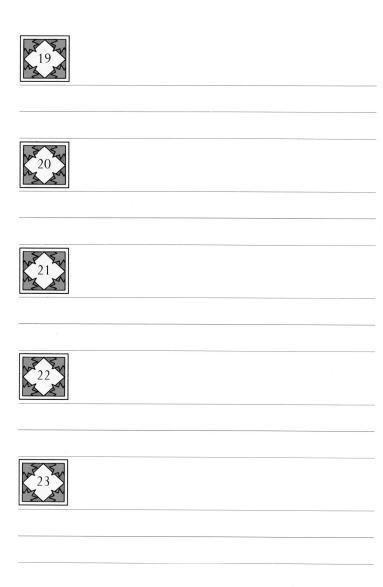

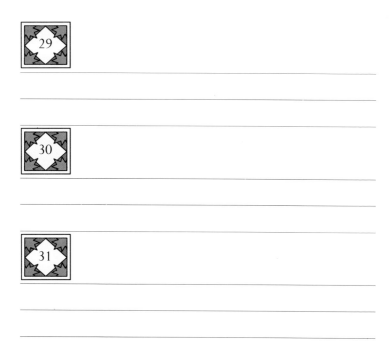

AUGUST

1

2

3

4

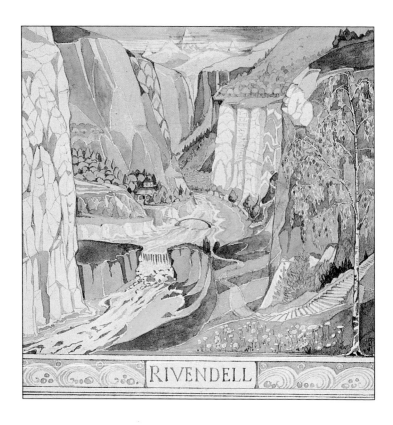

RIVENDELL

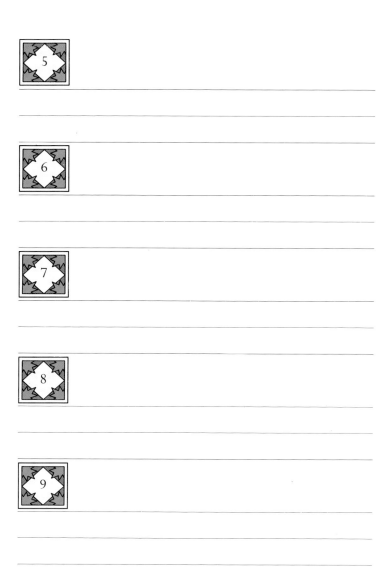

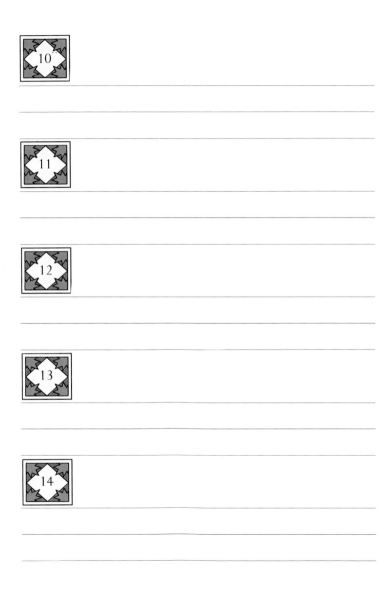

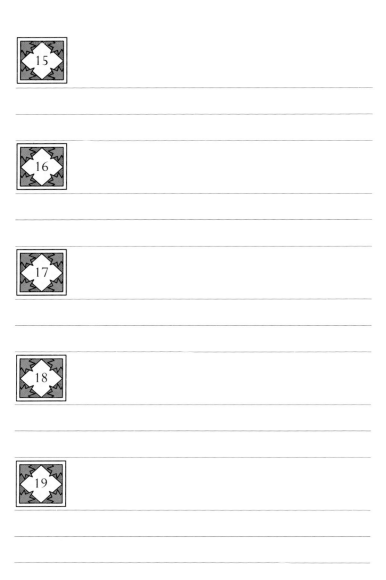

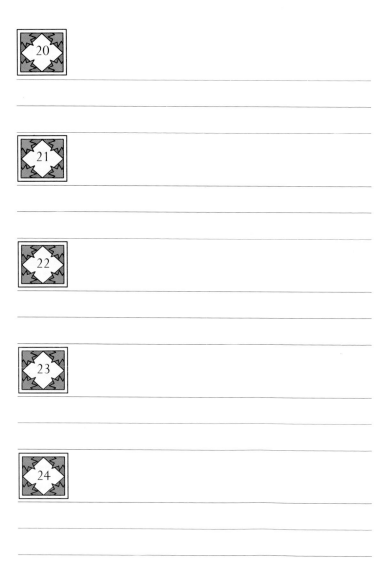

20

21

22

23

24

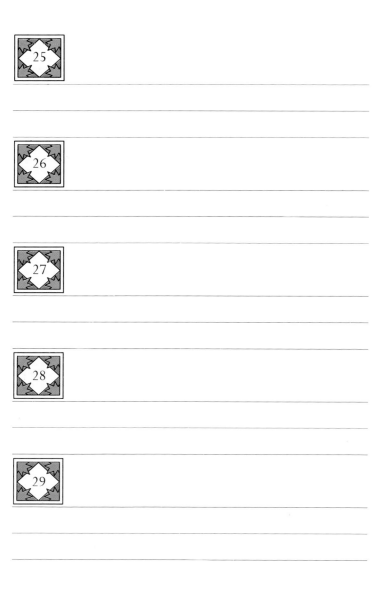

30

_____

_____

31

_____

_____

SEPTEMBER

1

2

3

4

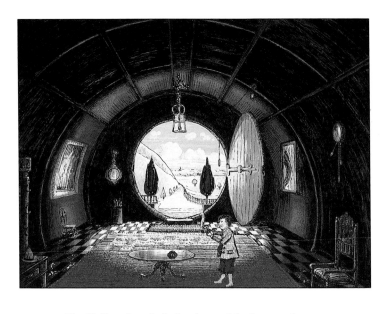

The Hall at Bag-End. Residence of B. Baggins Esquire.

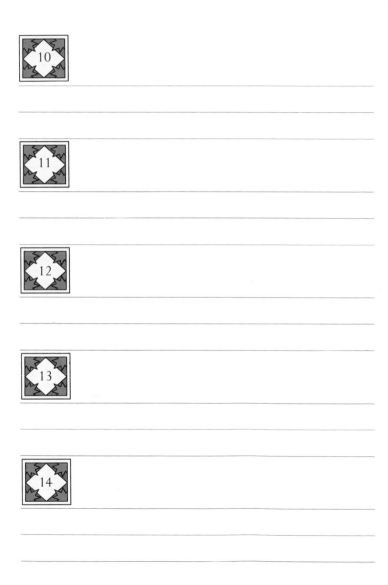

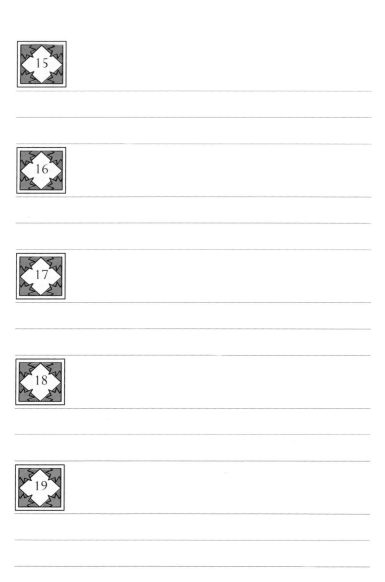

20

_____

_____

21

_____

_____

22

_____

_____

23

_____

_____

24

_____

_____

30

OCTOBER

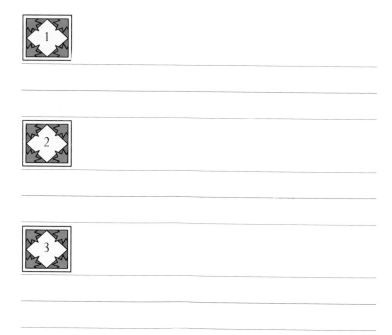

1

2

3

The Trolls

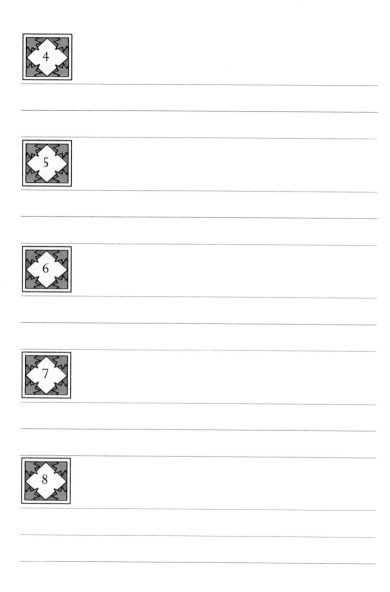

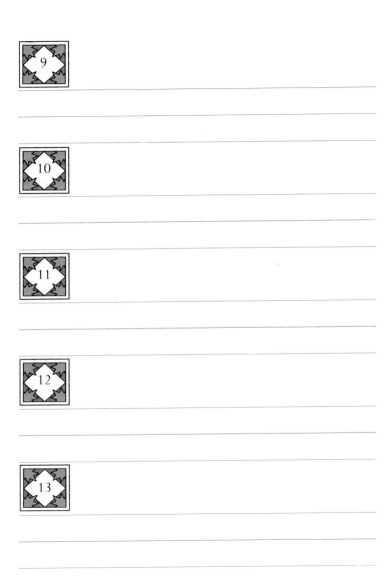

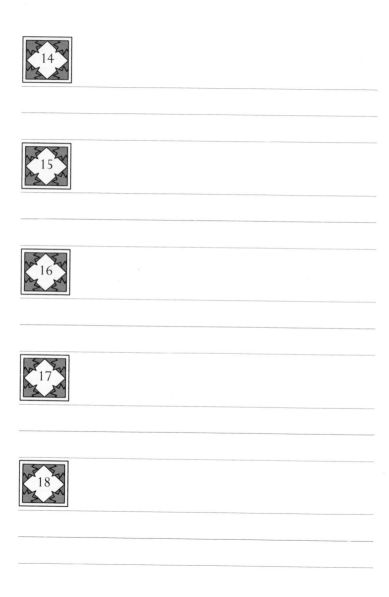

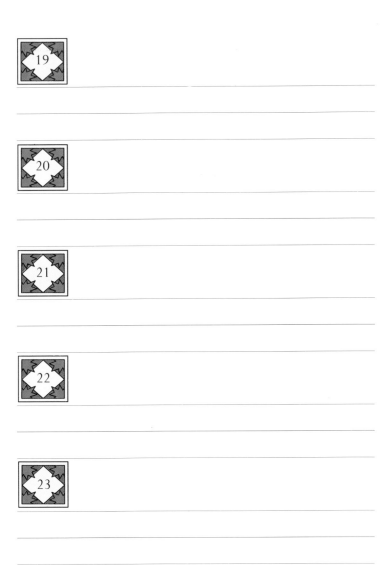

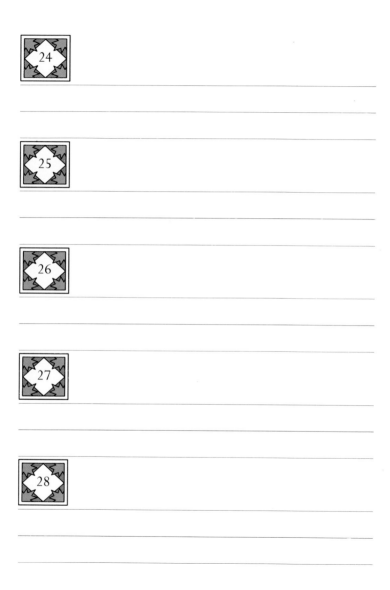

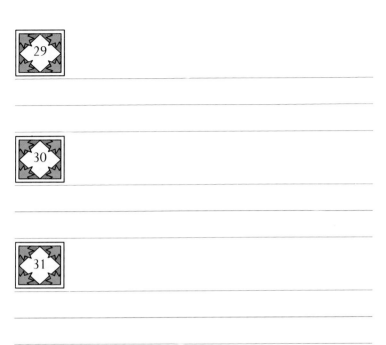

29

30

31

The Mountain Path

NOVEMBER

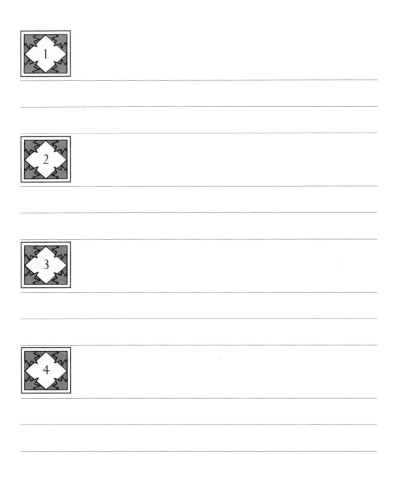

1

2

3

4

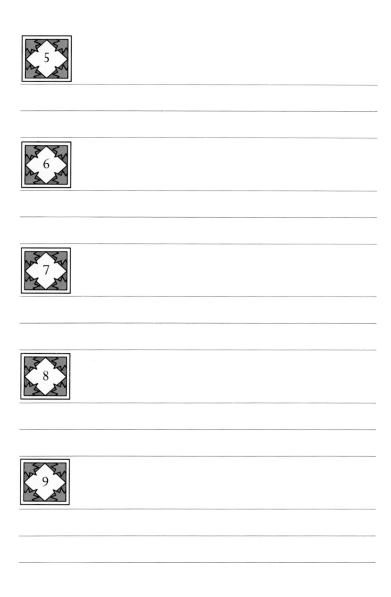

10

11

12

13

14

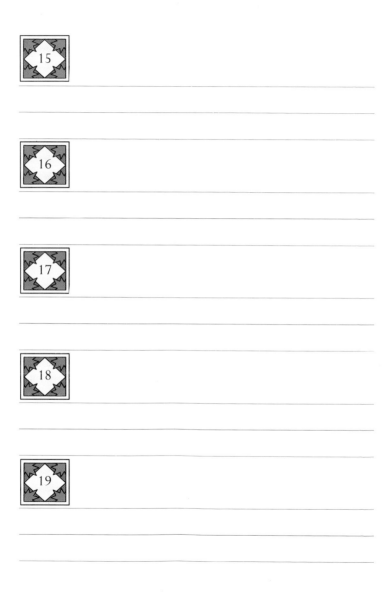

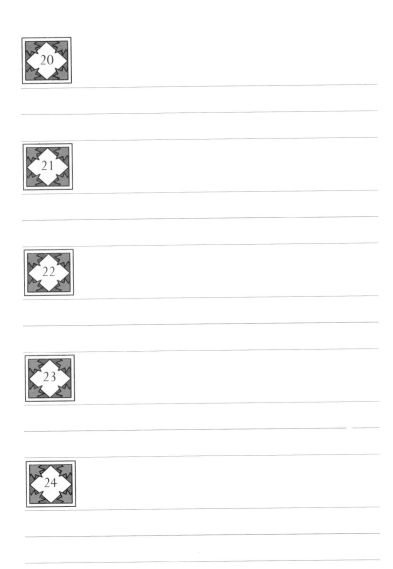

25

26

27

28

29

30

DECEMBER

1

2

3

BEORN'S HALL

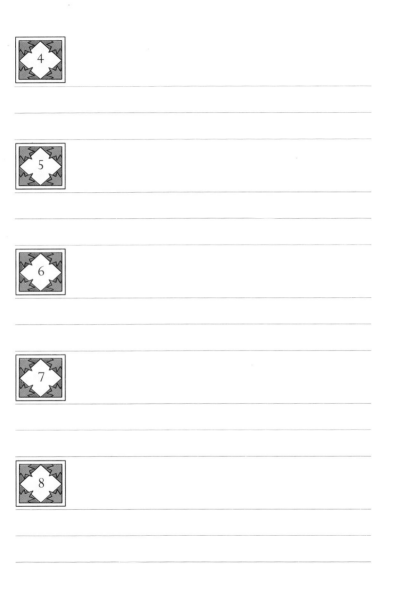

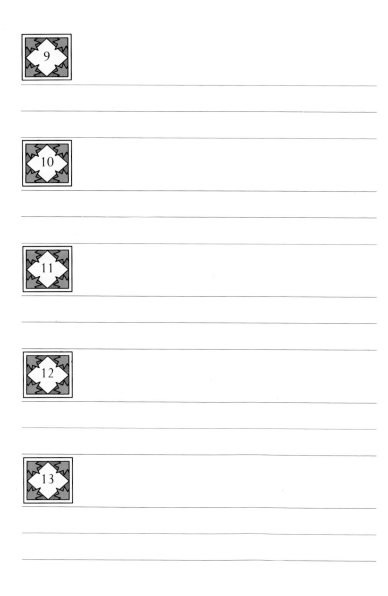

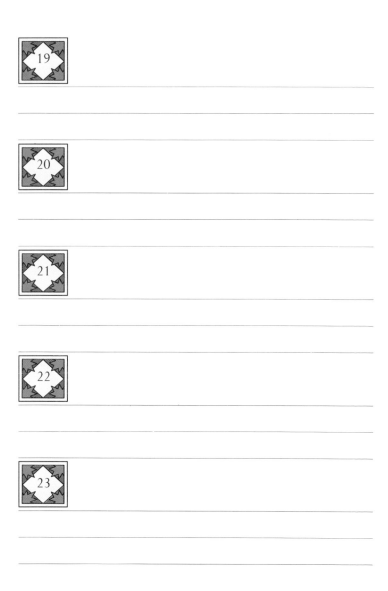

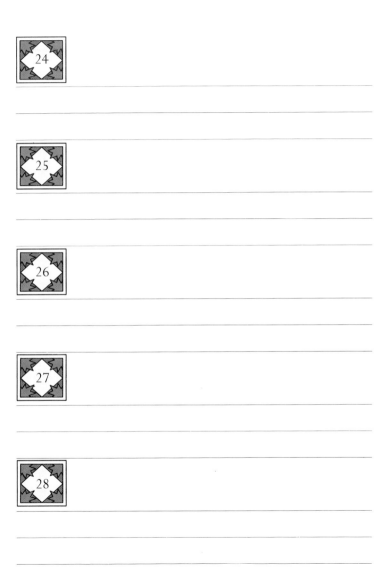

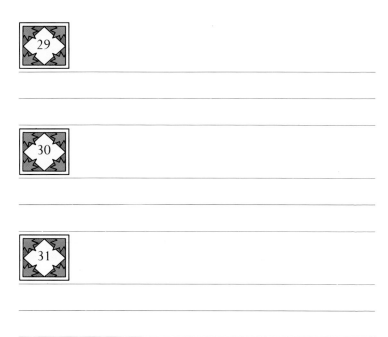

NOTES

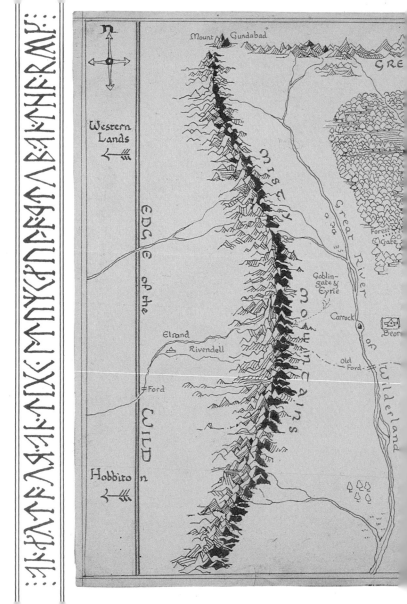